I'm Through!
What Can I Do?

Written by Linda Schwartz
Illustrated by Bev Armstrong

The Learning Works, Inc.

The Learning Works

Editor: Kimberley Clark
Illustrator: Bev Armstrong
Book Design: Clark Editorial & Design
Cover Illustrator: Karl Edwards
Cover Designer: Barbara Peterson
Project Director: Linda Schwartz

Contents

To the Teacher 5

Fun with Words

Compound Capers 6
More Compound Capers 7
Anagram Antics 8
More Anagram Antics 9
Palindrome Challenge 10
Find the Food 11
Hidden Animals 12
Mystery Message 13
Letter Links 14
More Letter Links 15
Groupies 16
Hide Five 17
Alphabet Soup 18

Number and Shape Puzzles

Beautiful Birds 19
Fabulous Fish 20
Number Roundup #1 21
Number Roundup #2 22
Score a Home Run .23
Find Five 24
Catch a Thief 25
Number Pattern Puzzle #1 26
Number Pattern Puzzle #2 27
Geometric Challenge 28
Pick a Set 29
Marathon Winner 30
Bingo Bongo 31

Picture Puzzles

Sort the Socks 32
Candy Match 33
Pizza Pieces 34
Matching Marbles 35
Bagel, Bongo, and Bounce 36
I See! 37
Legs and No Legs 38
Separate the Sounds 39
Dinosaur Dig 40
Clever Creature 41
Flying High 42
Four-Legged Flier 43
Junk Drawer Jumble 44–45
Focus on the Flags 46–47
Jumbo Jet 48
Graph a Mantis 49
Seventeenth-Century Ship 50
Carousel Charger 51

I'm Through! What Can I Do? Gr. 5–6
© The Learning Works, Inc.

Contents
(continued)

Critical Thinking

What's Hot – What's Not 52
More What's Hot – What's Not 53
Odd Word Out 54
More Odd Word Out 55
Nature Category Game 56
Geography Category Game 57
Leisure Time Category Game 58
Just for Fun Category Game 59
The Bolobo Bug 60
Choose the Shoes 61
Mitzi la Foo–Foo 62–63
The Bird Watcher 64–65
Mystery Vacation 66
Elegant Eggs 67

Creative Thinking

Make an M 68
Create a Word 69
The Invention Convention 70
Pet Problems 71
Create a Superhero 72
Ice Cream Ideas 73
Foot Fashion Fun 74
Lively Lizard 75
Design a Robot 76
Descriptions 77

Just for Fun

Complete a Cheetah 78
Half a Mask 79
Draw a Dump Truck 80
Picture a Player 81
Sketch a Siamese Cat 82
Design a Daisy 83
Fish Grid 84
Bird Grid 85
Motorcycle Mosaic 86
Mammoth Moth 87
Nail Maze 88
Shoelace Race 89
Through the Turtle 90
Web Site 91

Answer Key 92–96

To the Teacher

The activities in this book are the perfect solution for kids who finish class assignments early and ask, "I'm through! What can I do?" They are ideal for extra credit and homework assignments as well as learning center activities. They can also be used to fill those extra minutes of transition time during the school day.

The book is packed with puzzles, brainteasers, pictures to draw, and mazes. It includes the following sections:

- Fun with Words
- Number and Shape Puzzles
- Picture Puzzles
- Critical Thinking
- Creative Thinking
- Just for Fun

The activities are creative, challenging, and fun! Best of all, they can be done independently by students. This makes them perfect for those times when you're busy with a reading group or working with other students. The activities and puzzles can also be used as rewards and incentives.

The activities correlate to the curriculum and cover reading, vocabulary, writing, math, and more. These ready-to-use puzzles are just what you as a busy teacher need to keep your students challenged and your classroom humming.

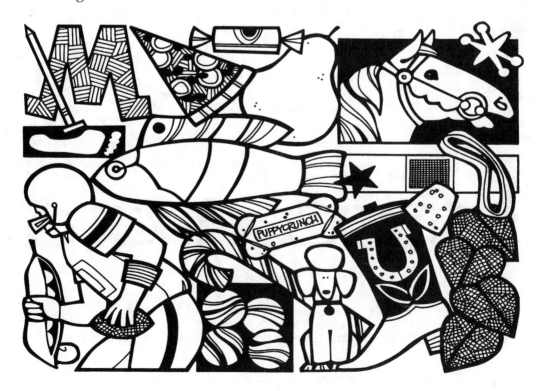

Name _____

Compound Capers

A *compound* word is made by combining two or more words such as **fire** and **place** to make **fireplace**. On each line, write a word that can be used to *end* the word on the left and *start* the word on the right to form two compound words.

example: bubble __*gum*__ drop (bubblegum – gumdrop)

1. horse   _____   pack
2. base   _____   park
3. count   _____   town
4. ant   _____   top
5. dish   _____   cake
6. every   _____   time
7. outer   _____   station
8. grape   _____   yard
9. wheel   _____   lift
10. day   _____   fast
11. fire   _____   mat
12. waste   _____   ball
13. road   _____   age
14. light   _____   boat
15. copy   _____   fish

Just for Fun

Make up five "Compound Capers" of your own for a friend to solve.

Name _____

More Compound Capers

A *compound* word is made by combining two or more words such as **fire** and **place** to make **fireplace**. On each line, write a word that can be used to *end* the word on the left and *start* the word on the right to form two compound words.

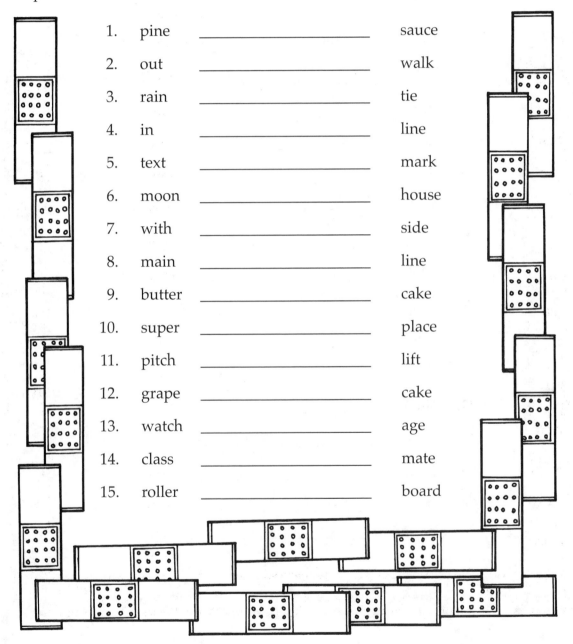

1.	pine	_____	sauce
2.	out	_____	walk
3.	rain	_____	tie
4.	in	_____	line
5.	text	_____	mark
6.	moon	_____	house
7.	with	_____	side
8.	main	_____	line
9.	butter	_____	cake
10.	super	_____	place
11.	pitch	_____	lift
12.	grape	_____	cake
13.	watch	_____	age
14.	class	_____	mate
15.	roller	_____	board

Just for Fun

Make up five "Compound Capers" of your own for a friend to solve.

I'm Through! What Can I Do? Gr. 5–6
© The Learning Works, Inc.

Name _____

Anagram Antics

An *anagram* is a word formed by rearranging the letters of one word to create another word without adding or subtracting any letters.

example: **scare** – *races, cares, acres*

Write an anagram for each word below.

1. lead _____

2. ache _____

3. throw _____

4. wrong _____

5. read _____

6. horse _____

7. cape _____

8. notes _____

9. drapes _____

10. pears _____

11. thing _____

12. stale _____

13. trace _____

14. desert _____

15. master _____

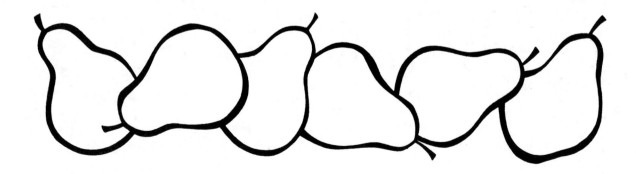

Name _____

More Anagram Antics

An *anagram* is a word formed by rearranging the letters of one word to create another word without adding or subtracting any letters.

example: **spare** *– reaps, pears, spear*

Write an anagram for each word below.

1. used _____

2. star _____

3. acres _____

4. meat _____

5. bear _____

6. danger _____

7. snare _____

8. clean _____

9. secure _____

10. least _____

11. skate _____

12. parts _____

13. grate _____

14. share _____

15. notices _____

Just for Fun

Create a list of five or more "Anagram Antics"
for a friend to solve.

I'm Through! What Can I Do? Gr. 5–6
© The Learning Works, Inc.

Name _____

Palindrome Challenge

A *palindrome* is a word or group of words that reads
the same both forward and backward.

examples: *bib, radar, noon*

Take the challenge, and see if you can list 10 or more palindromes
on the lines below. Use the back of this paper if you need more room.

_____   _____
_____   _____
_____   _____
_____   _____
_____   _____

How many groups of words or sentences can you write that are palindromes?
Use the back of this paper if you need more room.

examples: *we sew*
             A dog – a panic in a pagoda!
             A man, a plan, a canal – Panama!

_____

_____

Name _____

Find the Food

The name of a food is hidden in each sentence below. The letters are all in the correct order, but are found in two or more words. Underline the name of each food you find. Use the list of words in the box at the bottom of the page if you need help finding a food. The first one has been done for you.

1. Either Ma<u>c or N</u>ed will be on your team. (corn)

2. Will you sip each flavor and tell me which one you like best?

3. Please give this note to Mat on your way home today.

4. When I return, I plan to take you to see the new movie.

5. If I shout too much during the football game, let me know.

6. Mom likes to go to a store when there is a sale so she can save money.

7. Silver hoop earrings will look great with her outfit.

8. Come to the depot at once; the train is arriving in five minutes.

9. A bumblebee flew into the car while Mom was driving.

10. Dad says we have to fumigate our house because we have termites.

11. The hardest questions could only be answered by a few students.

12. That man goes to work at exactly the same time every morning.

13. Rob, an anaconda, is my favorite animal in the zoo.

14. There is a problem on the freeway, and traffic is backed up for miles.

15. Loren asked, "Can Dylan go with me to the soccer game on Friday?"

Names of Foods Hidden in the Sentences				
banana	candy	lemon	pear	tofu
beans	corn	mango	potato	tomato
beef	fish	peach	toast	turnip

Just for Fun

Write three sentences and hide the name of a food in each one.
See if a friend can find your hidden foods.

I'm Through! What Can I Do? Gr. 5–6
© The Learning Works, Inc.

Name _____

Hidden Animals

The name of an animal is hidden in each sentence below. The letters are all in the correct order, but are found in two or more words. Underline the name of each animal you find. Use the list of words in the box at the bottom of the page if you need help finding an animal. The first one has been done for you.

1. Either Se<u>th or Se</u>lma will pick you up for practice this afternoon. (horse)

2. If you slam books on a table while in the library, you'll disturb everyone.

3. Hey, Leo, pardon the mess while the workers remodel your office.

4. We plan to go at 4:00 because we want to avoid the traffic.

5. The lab at the hospital just got money for six new microscopes.

6. Each awkward step the toddler took on its wobbly legs seemed like such an effort.

7. To be artistic, a person needs to have an eye for color and style.

8. The circus clown used a hoop and a horn in his act under the big top.

9. Did you notice that Jack always wears his favorite shirt on Monday?

10. They came late to the game because they got tied up in traffic.

11. Be a very good friend and let me borrow the notes you took in science class.

12. There are many bad germs that can cause flu-like symptoms.

13. Divers often find many lost riches when they explore sunken ships.

14. I can only wait a second or two for your answer before I have to call on someone else.

15. The teacher told us to add the four numbers to get the sum.

Name of Animals Hidden in the Sentences

badger	beaver	goat	jackal	ostrich
bat	camel	hawk	lamb	panda
bear	condor	horse	leopard	toad

Name _____

Mystery Message

If you follow the directions correctly, a mystery message will appear. Read the message from top to bottom and left to right, and write it on the lines at the bottom of the page.

CHAIR	GOLF	TATTLE	YOU
FUNNY	CAN'T	DECIDED	BOWLING
SCHOOL	JUDGE	WHEW	BANANAS
BENCH	PENCIL	A	PEACH
BOOK	CORN	RUGBY	DINED
LETTER	OH	INSIDE	BY
JUDO	DELIVERED	ITS	WOW
COUCH	COVER	POLO	SUPPER

- Cross off all words that begin and end with the letter D.
- Cross off all words that have two identical consonants together.
- Cross off all words that have exactly six letters.
- Cross off all words that are names of foods.
- Cross off all words that are things you can sit on.
- Cross off all words that are interjections.
- Cross off all words that are names of sports.

Mystery Message

_____

_____

I'm Through! What Can I Do? Gr. 5–6
© The Learning Works, Inc.

Name _____

Letter Links

How many words of three or more letters can you make by moving one square at a time in any direction? You may not use a letter twice in a row, but plurals are allowed. Write the words on the lines below. Use the back of the paper if you need more room. Hint: There are more than 35 words!

K	N	S
I	E	W
T	R	A

knew

_____   _____

_____   _____

_____   _____

_____   _____

_____   _____

_____   _____

_____   _____

_____   _____

_____   _____

_____   _____

_____   _____

_____   _____

_____   _____

_____   _____

_____   _____

_____   _____

_____   _____

_____   _____

More Letter Links

How many words of three or more letters can you make by moving one square at a time in any direction? You may not use a letter twice in a row. Write the words on the lines below. Use the back of the paper if you need more room. Hint: There are more than 60 words!

B	R	E
U	A	G
C	I	N
H	M	T

_____ grain _____   _____

_____   _____

_____   _____

_____   _____

_____   _____

_____   _____

_____   _____

_____   _____

_____   _____

_____   _____

_____   _____

_____   _____

_____   _____

_____   _____

I'm Through! What Can I Do? Gr. 5–6
© The Learning Works, Inc.

Name _____

Groupies

Each set of three words can be matched with a fourth word to make a *groupie*. This fourth word can be added to the front or back of all three words. For each set of words, write the word that makes a groupie. The first one has been done for you.

1. _____**life**_____   boat   time   jacket

2. _____   plant   hold   green

3. _____   ware   ship   boiled

4. _____   lash   glasses   brow

5. _____   stroke   pack   stop

6. _____   mate   room   work

7. _____   keep   lift   set

8. _____   fall   melon   front

9. _____   town   stairs   grade

10. _____   hear   grown   throw

11. _____   store   end   mark

12. _____   light   chair   rise

Just for Fun

Make up five "Groupies" to share with a friend.

Name _____

Hide Five

Each of these three-letter words can be found in five or more longer words. For example, *are* is found in *arena, spare, hare, care, prepare,* and *careful*. List the longer words under each three-letter word. If you need more room, use the back of your paper.

pea
_____
_____
_____
_____
_____

tin
_____
_____
_____
_____
_____

ear
_____
_____
_____
_____
_____

tea
_____
_____
_____
_____
_____

her
_____
_____
_____
_____
_____

his
_____
_____
_____
_____
_____

I'm Through! What Can I Do? Gr. 5–6
© The Learning Works, Inc.

Name _____

Alphabet Soup

How many words of three or more letters can you make
from the letters in the words *alphabet soup*?

Rules:

- No proper nouns are allowed.

- Plural words are allowed.

- You may only use a letter the number of times it appears in alphabet soup. (For example, *set* is okay but *sets* is not because there is only one "s.")

There are more than 120 possible words. How many can you find?
List your answers below. Use the back of your paper if you need more room.

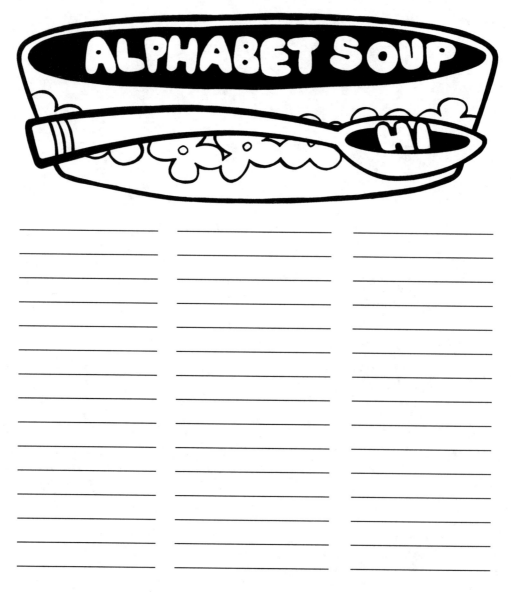

_____   _____   _____
_____   _____   _____
_____   _____   _____
_____   _____   _____
_____   _____   _____
_____   _____   _____
_____   _____   _____
_____   _____   _____
_____   _____   _____
_____   _____   _____
_____   _____   _____
_____   _____   _____

Name _____

Beautiful Birds

Work the problems, then color the birds according to the code below.

Answers ending in 0 = red   Answers ending in 4 = blue
Answers ending in 1 = yellow   Answers ending in 5 = blue-green
Answers ending in 2 = purple   Answers ending in 6 = yellow-green
Answers ending in 3 = green   Answers ending in 7 = orange

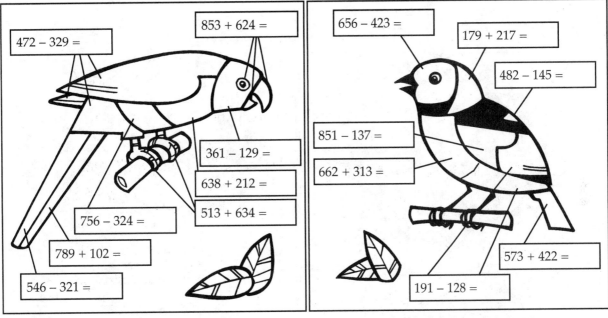

472 − 329 =

853 + 624 =

361 − 129 =

638 + 212 =

513 + 634 =

756 − 324 =

789 + 102 =

546 − 321 =

Rainbow Lory

656 − 423 =

179 + 217 =

482 − 145 =

851 − 137 =

662 + 313 =

573 + 422 =

191 − 128 =

Green-Headed Tanager

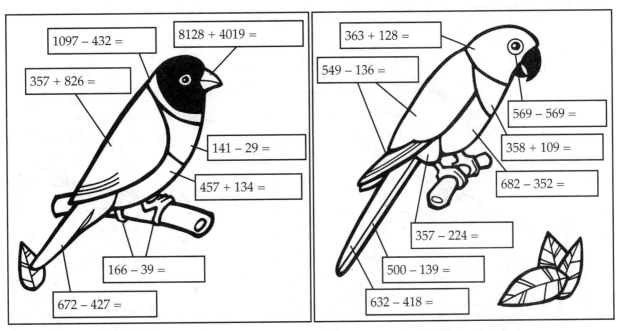

1097 − 432 =

8128 + 4019 =

357 + 826 =

141 − 29 =

457 + 134 =

166 − 39 =

672 − 427 =

Gouldian Finch

363 + 128 =

549 − 136 =

569 − 569 =

358 + 109 =

682 − 352 =

357 − 224 =

500 − 139 =

632 − 418 =

Sun Parakeet

I'm Through! What Can I Do? Gr. 5–6
© The Learning Works, Inc.

Name _____

Fabulous Fish

Work the problems, then color the fish according to the code below.

Answers ending in 0 = red   Answers ending in 4 = blue
Answers ending in 1 = yellow   Answers ending in 5 = blue-green
Answers ending in 2 = purple   Answers ending in 6 = yellow-green
Answers ending in 3 = light blue   Answers ending in 7 = orange

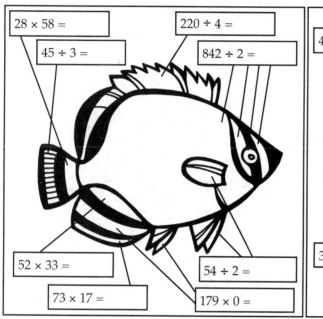

28 × 58 =
45 ÷ 3 =
220 ÷ 4 =
842 ÷ 2 =
52 × 33 =
54 ÷ 2 =
73 × 17 =
179 × 0 =

Redfin Butterflyfish

45 × 15 =
869 ÷ 869 =
35 ÷ 7 =
33 × 15 =
117 × 9 =
440 ÷ 4 =

Leave unlabeled areas white.

Powder-Blue Surgeonfish

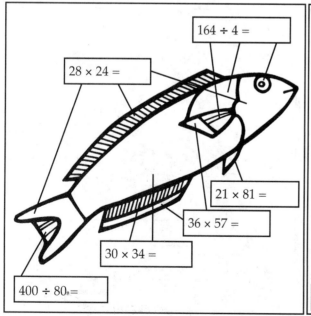

164 ÷ 4 =
28 × 24 =
21 × 81 =
36 × 57 =
30 × 34 =
400 ÷ 80 =

Rainbow Wrasse

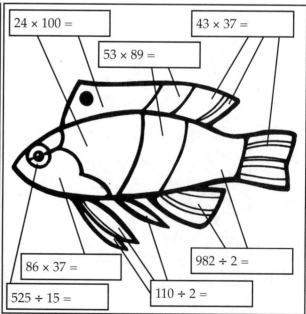

24 × 100 =
43 × 37 =
53 × 89 =
86 × 37 =
525 ÷ 15 =
110 ÷ 2 =
982 ÷ 2 =

Royal Gramma

Name _____

Number Roundup #1

```
7 1 4 3 7 1 0 4 5 6
2 4 5 0 6 9 9 2 2 6
0 6 0 3 5 1 7 8 2 3
3 0 8 4 2 6 4 0 4 8
6 8 7 5 1 1 6 5 6 0
2 9 3 8 3 0 6 1 8 7
5 4 9 4 5 8 4 1 0 2
1 6 3 5 7 1 5 3 5 4
5 0 4 3 8 6 2 2 2 1
2 8 7 9 1 2 7 6 0 1
```

This search puzzle uses numbers instead of letters.
Find and circle the following numbers going across, down, diagonally,
forwards, and backwards in the puzzle. Can you find all 24?

03625	32161	56873	80724
04386	35178	63571	83476
10456	42805	64527	85126
12534	46089	65213	97466
24680	50873	75116	99226
28791	51132	74041	97067

I'm Through! What Can I Do? Gr. 5–6
© The Learning Works, Inc.

Name _____

Number Roundup #2

```
8 9 7 4 0 1 3 5 2 1 7 4
9 1 3 0 6 4 5 3 1 9 1 5
3 0 7 1 5 4 2 7 9 0 5 3
0 8 4 8 2 3 0 1 8 2 7 6
7 5 4 5 0 2 1 8 4 3 1 5
6 5 6 4 0 8 2 6 3 1 0 9
3 0 1 3 1 7 6 9 5 3 2 1
5 3 9 7 0 1 3 2 5 3 7 6
7 4 6 3 1 1 8 6 4 5 9 7
8 9 7 0 1 7 2 5 3 4 1 2
7 1 3 1 0 8 9 6 3 5 4 9
1 8 2 9 5 2 5 0 7 1 6 8
```

This search puzzle uses numbers instead of letters.
Find and circle the following numbers going across, down, diagonally,
forwards, and backwards in the puzzle. Can you find all 30?

02791	23230	40185	61456	81136
05259	23769	45369	63109	88014
08624	26530	49302	63571	89276
11139	30131	50110	76953	91085
17808	30645	53970	79053	93076
19563	31769	54329	79911	97017

Just for Fun

Make up a "Number Roundup" puzzle for a friend to solve.
Create an answer key for your puzzle.

52985613785316928073251

Name _____

Score a Home Run

Score a home run by placing the numbers 2-9 in the squares below so that the sums of the numbers along each baseline equal 16. Each number can be used one time only.

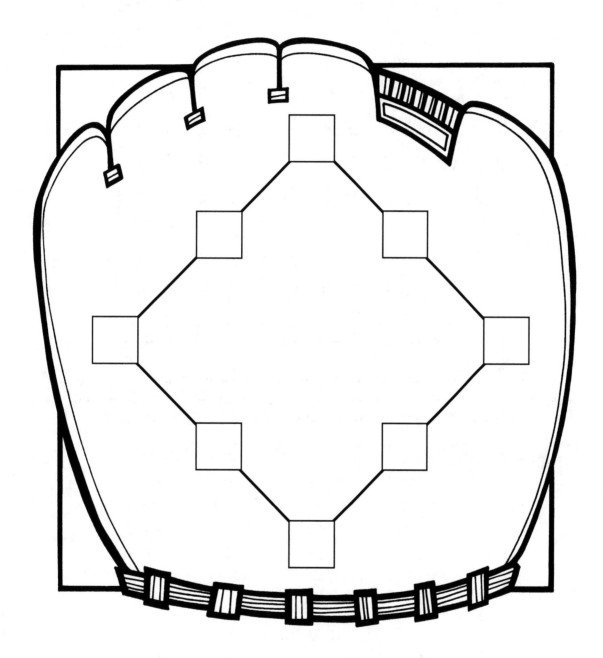

Just for Fun

Make up another puzzle using the same shape, but with different numbers and a different sum. Give your puzzle to a friend to solve.

Name _____

Find Five

Can you arrange four same-sized squares in ways that create five different shapes? They may not overlap, and must touch side to side and corner to corner.

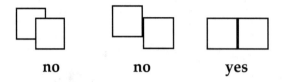

    no   **no**   **yes**

Each shape must be unique; the same shape drawn in two different positions counts as just one shape. Draw your shapes in the boxes below.

Name _____

Catch a Thief

Help Detective Donna and her trusty bloodhound find the person who made off with a priceless painting from the art museum. Footprints were left at the scene of the crime. If you follow the footprints and add the numbers along connecting paths to get the exact sum of 55, you can will catch the thief. Good luck!

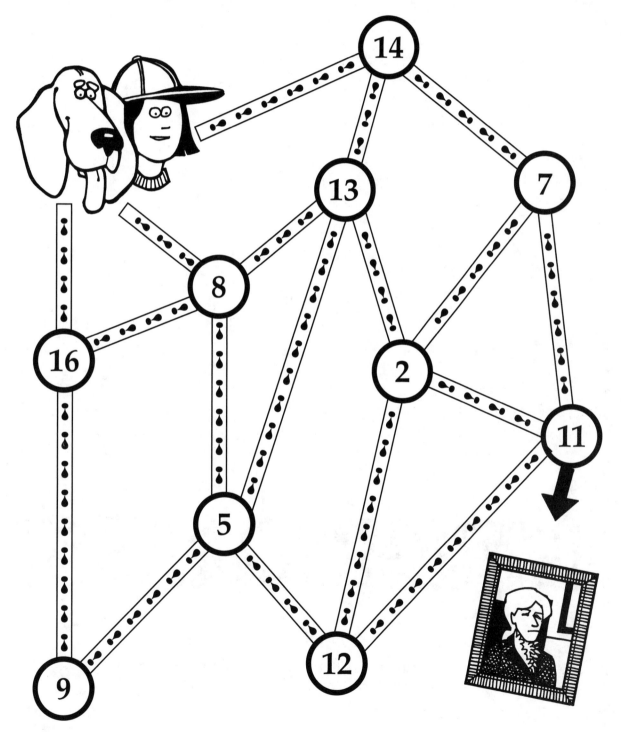

I'm Through! What Can I Do? Gr. 5–6
© The Learning Works, Inc.

Name _____

Number Pattern Puzzle #1

In each row, figure out the pattern of the number sequence, and write the missing number in the box. The first one has been done for you.

1.	27	28	30	31	33	34	36
2.	3	5	9	15	☐	33	45
3.	36	32	35	31	☐	30	33
4.	10	15	25	30	☐	45	55
5.	22	17	13	10	☐	7	7
6.	6	6	12	36	☐	720	4320
7.	7	13	26	32	☐	70	140
8.	84	42	168	84	☐	168	672
9.	77	67	56	44	☐	17	2
10.	4	16	80	40	☐	800	400

Just for Fun

Make up a number pattern puzzle for a friend to solve.
Create an answer key for your puzzle.

Name _____

Number Pattern Puzzle #2

In each row, figure out the pattern of the number sequence, and write the missing number in the box. The first one has been done for you.

1.	1	3	9	27	**81**	243	729
2.	88	83	78	73		63	58
3.	90	84	79	75		70	69
4.	12	14	18	24		42	54
5.	76	68	60	52		36	28
6.	50	54	53	57		60	59
7.	11	16	12	17		18	14
8.	41	48	56	65		86	98
9.	100	88	76	64		40	28
10.	38	41	36	39		37	32

Just for Fun

Make up a number pattern puzzle for a friend to solve.
Create an answer key for your puzzle.

I'm Through! What Can I Do? Gr. 5–6
© The Learning Works, Inc.

Name _____

Geometric Challenge

Look at the geometric shapes below, and fill in the blanks.

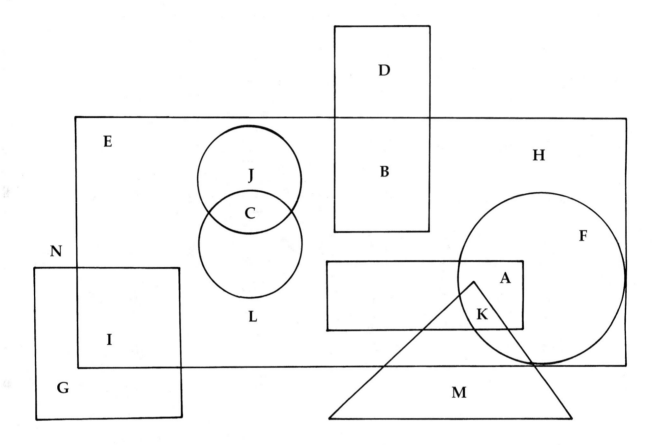

1. Which letters are in a circle and the large rectangle only? _____

2. Which letters are in the large rectangle only? _____

3. Which letter is in a square and a rectangle? _____

4. Which letter is in two circles and a rectangle? _____

5. What letter is not in any shape? _____

6. What letter is in a triangle only? _____

7. What letter is in a circle and two rectangles? _____

8. What letter is in two rectangles, two triangles, and a circle? _____

9. What letter is in a large and small rectangle only? _____

10. What letters are in one shape only? _____

Name _____

Pick a Set

Find two boxes that have the exact same numbers and math symbols.
Fill in the answers at the bottom of the page.

1. 4 × 3 7 9 2 ÷ 8 5 + 6	**2.** ÷ 5 × 2 3 8 4 + 9 6
3. 9 5 + 3 4 7 8 × 6	**4.** 8 2 ÷ 7 3 6 5 9 + 4
5. × 4 + 2 5 ÷ 8 9 3 6	**6.** 5 + 4 2 6 × 3 ÷ 8 7

The two matching boxes are _____ and _____ .

I'm Through! What Can I Do? Gr. 5–6
© The Learning Works, Inc.

Name _____

Marathon Winner

These marathon runners have just passed the finish line. Look at the numbers that they are wearing. The winner's number has two odd digits and two even digits and is divisible by 3. Color the winner.

Jan

Steve

Kendra

Mike

Cathy

Jamal

Juanita

Marco

Jessica

Name _____

Bingo Bongo

There are lots of numbers on the Bingo Bongo balls, but only five of them match a row on the card. Find the five numbers on the balls that match one row on the card going across, down, or diagonally. Color that row on the card and the five matching Bingo Bongo balls.

Balls: 48, 10, 95, 9, 19, 32, 77, 42, 67, 86, 15, 4, 46, 75, 52, 16, 72, 38, 21, 2, 51, 80, 24, 92, 70, 65, 8, 12, 47, 63, 84, 88

Bingo Bongo

24	12	84	16	55
92	78	46	32	21
3	51	72	48	86
67	80	9	95	4
19	52	33	65	47

I'm Through! What Can I Do? Gr. 5–6
© The Learning Works, Inc.

Name _____

Sort the Socks

There are 10 pairs of socks in this pile.
Find the pairs and color them so they match.

Name _____

Candy Match

Find and color the two identical pieces of candy in each bag.

A

B

C

D

I'm Through! What Can I Do? Gr. 5–6
© The Learning Works, Inc.

Name _____

Pizza Pieces

In each box, circle the two identical pieces of pizza.

A

B

C

Name _____

Matching Marbles

In each bag, two of the marbles are exactly the same.
Find those marbles and color them.

I'm Through! What Can I Do? Gr. 5–6
© The Learning Works, Inc.

Name _____

Bagel, Bongo, and Bounce

Draw a line to separate the dogs with five-letter names from the dogs whose names have six letters. Starting at dot A and ending at dot B, and drawing only straight lines, make a path connecting all the dots. You may not retrace or cross over a line or touch the same dot twice.

Name _____

I See!

Draw a line to separate the names of those items that contain the letter "i" from the names that do not contain the letter "i." Starting at dot A and ending at dot B, and drawing only straight lines, make a path connecting all the dots. You may not retrace or cross over a line or touch the same dot twice.

Name _____

Legs and No Legs

Draw a line to separate the things with legs from those without legs. Starting at dot A and ending at dot B, and drawing only straight lines, make a path connecting all the dots. You may not retrace or cross over a line or touch the same dot twice.

Name _____

Separate the Sounds

The names of some of these items end in consonants, and others end in vowels. Draw a line separating the items according to the endings of their names. Starting at dot A and ending at dot B, and drawing only straight lines, make a path connecting all the dots. You may not retrace or cross over a line or touch the same dot twice.

I'm Through! What Can I Do? Gr. 5–6
© The Learning Works, Inc.

Name _____

Dinosaur Dig

Corythosaurus is a dinosaur that lived in western Canada at the same time as *Tyrannosaurus* and *Triceratops*. Find the Corythosaurus buried below by shading the shapes with vowels in them.

Name _____

Clever Creature

Hidden below is a picture of an animal with a large brain and a beak like a parrot's. This animal can change color and unscrew jar lids. Find this creature by shading the shapes with even numbers.

Name _____

Flying High

Find the pole vaulter hidden below by shading the shapes with consonants.

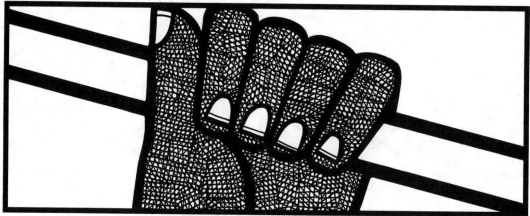

Name _____

Four-Legged Flier

Hidden below is an amphibian that glides between the trees of Asian rain forests. Find it by shading the shapes with two dots in them.

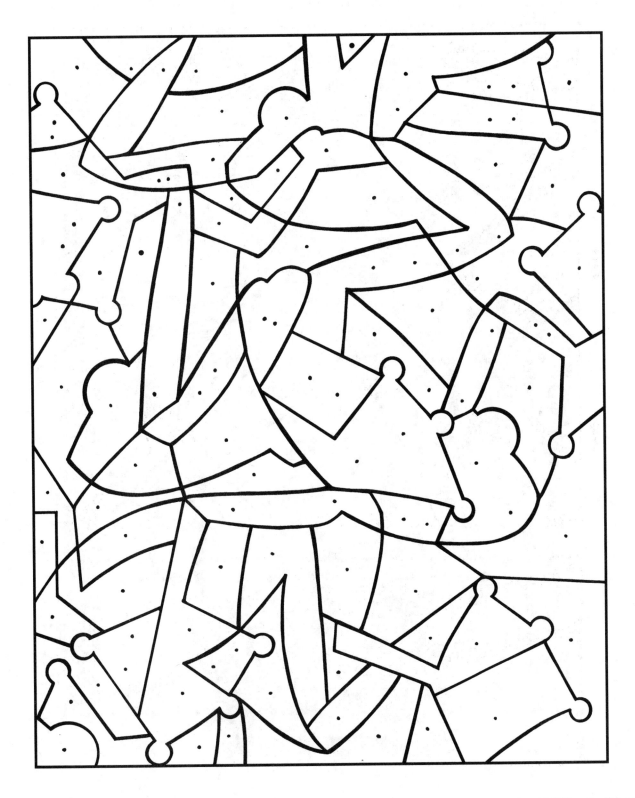

Name _____

Junk Drawer Jumble

Without looking at the checklist on page 45, carefully study the contents of this drawer for two minutes. Then hide this page, and use the checklist to record the things you remember seeing. Caution: There will be things on the list that are not in the drawer!

Name _____

Junk Drawer Jumble

After studying the junk drawer picture on page 44 for one minute, hide that page or turn it over. Then use this list to record all the things that you remember seeing. Think carefully: Eight things on this list are not in the drawer!

	acorn		fork		penny
	bandage		glue		price tag
	battery		golf ball		puzzle piece
	bolt		gum		rubber band
	bottle cap		jack		safety pin
	buckle		jingle bell		salt packet
	button		key		scissors
	candle		light bulb		seashell
	candy cane		lock		shoelace
	chain		matches		spool of thread
	clothespin		measuring spoon		stamp
	crayon		nail		straw
	dice		needle and thread		tape
	dog biscuit		paint brush		thimble
	dog license		paper clip		ticket
	eraser		peanut		toothbrush
	feather		pen		toy mouse
	fish food		pencil		whistle

I'm Through! What Can I Do? Gr. 5–6
© The Learning Works, Inc.

Name _____

Focus on the Flags

Study these flags carefully for two minutes, then answer
the questions on page 47 without looking at this page.

Canada

Cyprus

Israel

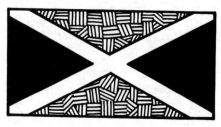

Jamaica

Lebanon

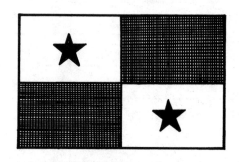

Panama

Rwanda

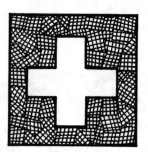

Switzerland

Name _____

Focus on the Flags

Answer these questions without looking at page 46.

1. Which country's flag has two black triangles? _____
2. Which two flags are more narrow than the others? _____
3. Which flag is divided into equal thirds? _____
4. Which flag is divided into equal fourths? _____
5. Which flag is square? _____
6. Which flag has a letter of the alphabet? _____
7. Which flag has two stars? _____
8. Which flag pictures the country it represents? _____
9. Which flag pictures a tree? _____
10. How many points are on the star on Israel's flag? _____

Canada • Cyprus • Israel • Jamaica
Lebanon • Panama • Rwanda • Switzerland

I'm Through! What Can I Do? Gr. 5–6
© The Learning Works, Inc.

Name _____

Jumbo Jet

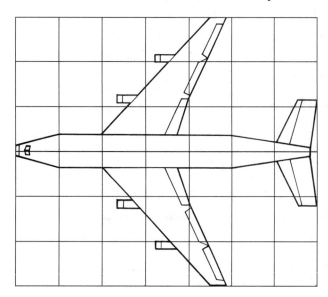

The Boeing 747 jumbo jet is more than 230 feet long, with a wingspan of 195 feet. Enlarge the small drawing on the left to the larger grid below.

Name _____

Graph a Mantis

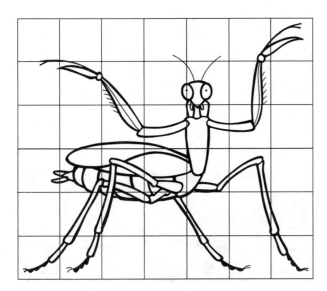

Enlarge the small drawing on the left to the larger grid below. To make your mantis look monstrous, add some inch tall people or tiny buildings and trees to your drawing.

I'm Through! What Can I Do? Gr. 5–6
© The Learning Works, Inc.

Name _____

Seventeenth-Century Ship

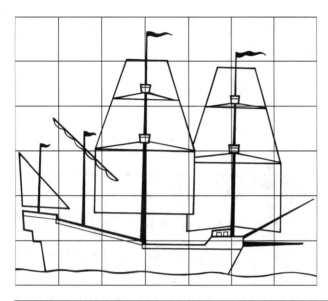

This English ship was 142 feet long. The *Pierre Guillaumat*, a modern oil tanker, is 1,359 feet long! Enlarge the drawing of the English ship to fit in the grid below.

Name _____

Carousel Charger

Enlarge the small drawing at left to fit in the grid below. You may wish to add more details, such as bells, tassels, fringe, and a design on the blanket.

Name _____

What's Hot – What's Not

The words in the "what's hot" column all have something in common. The words in the "what's not" column do not fit in the first group of words. Decide what the words in the first group have in common. On a separate sheet of paper, add two or more new words to each "what's hot" group.

What's Hot	**What's Not**
1. Ohio, Iowa, Alabama	Kansas, Texas, Washington
2. butter, corn, squash	tomato, asparagus, prune
3. turban, wig, helmet	collar, sleeve, sweatshirt
4. June, August, July	May, September, October
5. dad, weight, dish	repair, window, carpet
6. deed, level, shipyards	paper, open, boat
7. slippers, cleats, skis	skirts, ties, shirts
8. flan, leek, mousse	flaunt, leak, mouse
9. bucket, tray, bag	knife, phone, lamp
10. flour, rice, milk	pepper, coffee, jelly

Just for Fun

Make up your own "What's Hot – What's Not" for a friend to solve.

Name _____

More What's Hot – What's Not

The words in the "what's hot" column all have something in common. The words in the "what's not" column do not fit in the first group of words. Decide what the words in the first group have in common. On a separate sheet of paper, add two or more new words to each "what's hot" group.

What's Hot	**What's Not**
1. planet, marble, button	staple, book, pen
2. lettuce, peas, asparagus	carrot, banana, eggplant
3. flute, piccolo, oboe	harp, cello, tuba
4. Henry, Roger, Marco	Pete, Steve, Joe
5. look, heels, vacuum	wrote, jacket, lemon
6. many, youth, playmate	house, green, tiger
7. banner, little, cattle	teacher, picture, few
8. eyelid, anyone, goldfish	usually, test, nervous
9. damp, healthy, icy	and, have, there
10. about, stripe, open	window, dream, dog

Just for Fun

Make up your own "What's Hot – What's Not" for a friend to solve.

I'm Through! What Can I Do? Gr. 5–6
© The Learning Works, Inc.

Name _____

Odd Word Out

In each group of words, find and circle the word
that does not belong with the others.

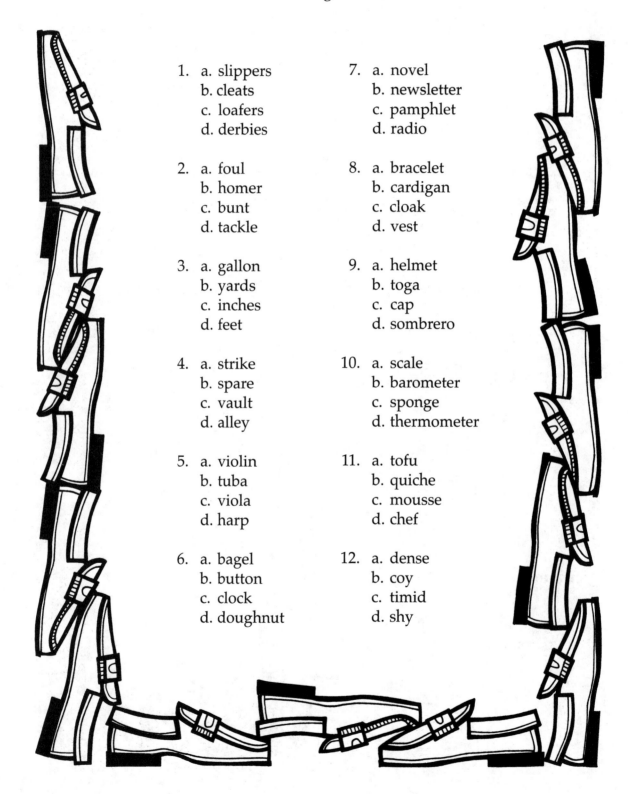

1. a. slippers
   b. cleats
   c. loafers
   d. derbies

2. a. foul
   b. homer
   c. bunt
   d. tackle

3. a. gallon
   b. yards
   c. inches
   d. feet

4. a. strike
   b. spare
   c. vault
   d. alley

5. a. violin
   b. tuba
   c. viola
   d. harp

6. a. bagel
   b. button
   c. clock
   d. doughnut

7. a. novel
   b. newsletter
   c. pamphlet
   d. radio

8. a. bracelet
   b. cardigan
   c. cloak
   d. vest

9. a. helmet
   b. toga
   c. cap
   d. sombrero

10. a. scale
    b. barometer
    c. sponge
    d. thermometer

11. a. tofu
    b. quiche
    c. mousse
    d. chef

12. a. dense
    b. coy
    c. timid
    d. shy

Name _____

More Odd Word Out

In each group of words, find and circle the word
that does not belong with the others.

1. a. triangle
    b. square
    c. radius
    d. rectangle

2. a. huddle
    b. putt
    c. touchdown
    d. kickoff

3. a. trout
    b. borzoi
    c. halibut
    d. carp

4. a. petunia
    b. sloth
    c. lynx
    d. gerbil

5. a. marble
    b. slate
    c. diamond
    d. gneiss

6. a. puck
    b. dribble
    c. hoop
    d. rebound

7. a. peony
    b. hibiscus
    c. crocus
    d. sycamore

8. a. cyclone
    b. palmetto
    c. humidity
    d. typhoon

9. a. lavender
    b. navy
    c. army
    d. cobalt

10. a. treble
    b. tambourine
    c. castanets
    d. cymbals

11. a. mouse
    b. rat
    c. keyboard
    d. chip

12. a. femur
    b. fibula
    c. scapula
    d. larynx

I'm Through! What Can I Do? Gr. 5–6
© The Learning Works, Inc.

Name _____

Nature Category Game

Think of a word in each category that begins with the letter on the left, and fill in the chart. Give yourself one point for each correct word going across each row. You can also earn one bonus point for each row going down where you have five correct answers and no blanks.

	mammal	bird	fish	flower	insect	score
S						
R						
L						
T						
M						
bonus points						total

Just for Fun

Make your own "Nature Category Game." Keep the same categories, but select five new letters to place in the boxes on the left.

Name _____

Geography Category Game

Think of a word in each category that begins with the letter on the left, and fill in the chart. Give yourself one point for each correct word going across each row. You can also earn one bonus point for each row going down where you have five correct answers and no blanks.

	city	body of water	geography term	mountain	score
B					
I					
C					
P					
O					
bonus points					**total**

I'm Through! What Can I Do? Gr. 5–6
© The Learning Works, Inc.

Name _____

Leisure Time Category Game

Think of a word in each category that begins with the letter on the left, and fill in the chart. Give yourself one point for each correct word going across each row. You can also earn one bonus point for each row going down where you have eight correct answers and no blanks.

	sport/game	movie	book title	song title	T.V. show	score
H						
B						
F						
C						
R						
S						
G						
P						
bonus points						total

Name _____

Just for Fun Category Game

Think of a word in each category that begins with the letter on the left, and fill in the chart. Give yourself one point for each correct word going across each row. You can also earn one bonus point for each row going down where you have five correct answers and no blanks.

	vegetable or fruit	items found in the kitchen	girl's name	boy's name	color	score
G						
W						
T						
O						
I						
P						
B						
R						
bonus points						total

Name _____

The Bolobo Bug

Imagine that you are an entomologist studying insects in the tropics hoping to find the rare bolobo bug. You suddenly come across a swarm of creepy-crawlies. You whip out your bug book and read the description of the bolobo bug. The bolobo bug:

- has spots
- has two long antennae
- has six legs
- has two wings
- has a fat body

- has a round head
- has small, beady eyes
- has a sharp stinger at the end of its body
- makes a sound that rhymes with " fizz"

Use the clues to eliminate one bug at a time.

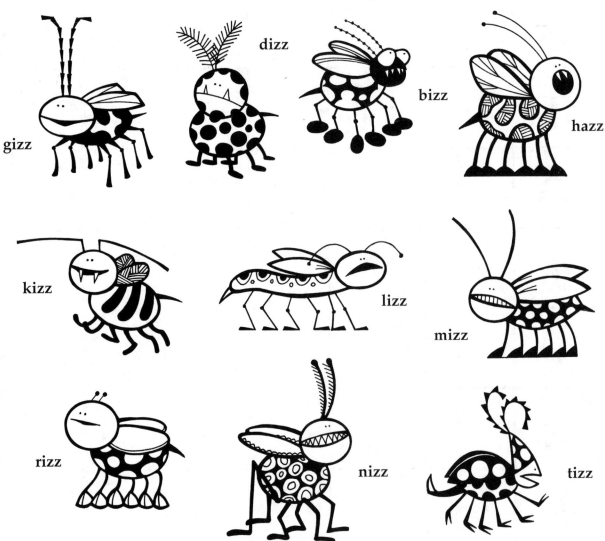

Circle the bolobo bug and write what it is saying. _____

Name _____

Choose the Shoes

Your old athletic shoes are falling apart, so it's time to head to the store to buy a new pair. Use the clues below to eliminate one style at a time, and circle the name of the shoes you end up buying.

Blizzard **Cyclone** **Earthquake**
Hurricane **Lightning** **Thunder**
Tornado **Typhoon** **Whirlwind**

Clues

- Your new shoes must have thick rubber on the bottom to cushion your feet when you play basketball.

- You'd like your new shoes to have a star on them.

- You prefer athletic shoes that have a stripe down the side.

- You don't want high-top shoes.

- You don't like polka-dotted shoelaces!

- You want mesh on the shoe so air can reach your feet.

- You prefer black soles because they don't show the dirt as much as white soles.

- Your new shoes must have a reflector for night jogging.

I'm Through! What Can I Do? Gr. 5–6
© The Learning Works, Inc.

Name _____

Mitzi la Foo–Foo

Mitzi la Foo-Foo, the notorious jewel thief, robbed The Jewelry Box yesterday in broad daylight. Police investigating the crime scene interviewed witnesses who saw her as she drove off in her red sports car. Use the information witnesses gave police to decide which woman on page 63 is Mitzi la Foo-Foo.

Name _____

Mitzi la Foo–Foo

Which of these suspects matches the descriptions given by the witnesses? ☐

I'm Through! What Can I Do? Gr. 5–6
© The Learning Works, Inc.

Name _____

The Bird Watcher

Mrs. Ima Byrd Watcher has just spotted a bird through her binoculars! Which bird did she discover? Find out by using the clues to eliminate one bird at a time on page 65 until only one bird is left. Color the bird Mrs. Ima Byrd Watcher saw.

Clues

- The bird's name has more than four letters.

- The bird's name does not start and end with a vowel.

- The bird's name does not have more than 10 letters in its name.

- The bird she saw does not contain the name of a color.

- The name of the bird does not rhyme with *lift*.

- The bird's name does not start with a consonant and end with a vowel.

- The name of the bird Ima saw does not start with the twentieth letter of the alphabet.

- The first three letters of the bird's name do not spell the name of a pronoun.

Name _____

The Bird Watcher

swift

hummingbird

thrush

grebe

oriole

crow

bluebird

cardinal

heron

I'm Through! What Can I Do? Gr. 5–6
© The Learning Works, Inc.

Name _____

Mystery Vacation

Where is the Clark family going for vacation? Find out by using the clues to eliminate one state at a time.

Clues

- We're not going to the state directly east of Tennessee.

- We're not going to the state directly north of Oregon.

- We're not headed for the state whose state song is "Yankee Doodle."

- We're not headed for the state that was the first one to be admitted to the Union in 1787.

- We're not headed for the state whose state flower is the camellia.

- We're not going to the smallest of the 50 states.

- We're not going to the state that is the largest in square miles.

- We're not going to the state known as the "Badger State."

- We're not going to the state whose capital is Austin.

- We're not going to the state whose state tree is the magnolia.

Alabama	Maine	Rhode Island
Alaska	Mississippi	Texas
Connecticut	North Carolina	Washington
Delaware		Wisconsin

The Clark family is headed for the state of _____ .

Critical Thinking

Name _____

Elegant Eggs

Read the clues to find the owners of the eggs.
Write the names in the spaces on the eggs.

- Eddie's egg doesn't have a house.
- Elena's egg doesn't have a star.
- Eli's egg doesn't have a leaf.
- Elisa's doesn't have a bird.
- Elmo's egg doesn't have a sun.
- Emma's egg doesn't have a heart.
- Eric's egg doesn't have a ladybug.
- Ernie's egg doesn't have a butterfly.
- Eseza's egg doesn't have a flower.
- Evan's egg doesn't have a worm.

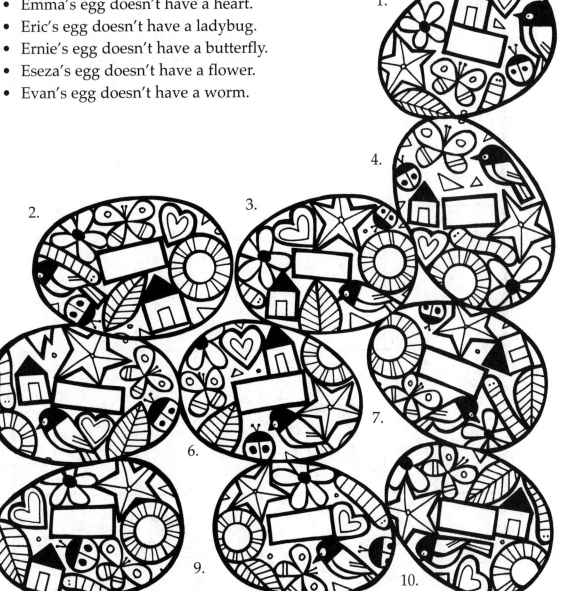

I'm Through! What Can I Do? Gr. 5–6
© The Learning Works, Inc.

Name _____

Make an M

How many different ways can you write the letter *M*?
Look at the examples below, and then add your own
original versions of the letter *M* in each of the empty boxes.

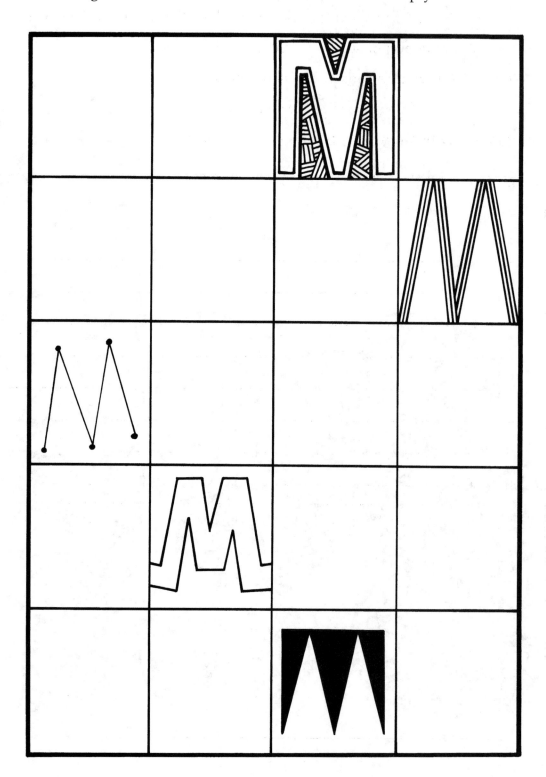

Name _____

Create a Word

- Make up a new word—one that's not found in the dictionary.

- Write your word below on the top line.

- Divide your word into syllables, and show where the accent mark belongs.

- Write the correct part of speech for your word.

- Tell what your word means in a sentence or two.

- Draw a picture of your word in the empty box.

- Use your new word in a sentence and underline it.

I'm Through! What Can I Do? Gr. 5–6
© The Learning Works, Inc.

Name _____

The Invention Convention

Congratulations! You have been selected to represent your state at the national invention convention. Draw a picture of the invention you will present. Label all the parts, and write a brief description of your clever device.

Name _____

Pet Problems

Your pet poodle, parakeet, python, and pig don't get along very well.
Design and label a new outdoor living area for them in the box below.

Name _____

Create a Superhero

Create a comic strip featuring an animal as the superhero. Write the title of the comic strip in the first box on the left. Then tell a short story in the boxes using cartoon illustrations. If you have ideas for more stories, write a comic book featuring your superhero.

ZAP! CRASH! POW! THUD! WHAM! TWANG!

Name _____

Ice Cream Ideas

Brainstorm ideas for new ice cream flavors. List each idea in a scoop below.
Name and describe these exciting, delicious new flavors.

Just for Fun

Of all the flavors you listed, which is your favorite?
Imagine that you have been selected to write a jingle or
song about this fantastic new flavor for a radio commercial.
Write your radio commercial on a separate sheet of paper.

I'm Through! What Can I Do? Gr. 5–6

Name _____

Foot Fashion Fun

Be a trend setter! Design a new foot fashion that is sure to become a fad with kids your age. It could be socks, an athletic shoe, swim fins, sandals, or even jewelry designed to be worn on the feet. Let your imagination soar!

In the space below, design an advertisement to sell your new creation in a teen magazine. Include a colored drawing of your foot fashion and creative ad copy that will make kids want to rush right out to buy it!

Name _____

Lively Lizard

A large, lively lizard has found its way into your room and is hiding under your bed. You want to keep it for a pet, but your mom insists that you capture it and take it outside. On the lines below, list ways to get this lively lizard out from under the bed without hurting it.

_____

_____

_____

_____

_____

_____

_____

_____

_____

_____

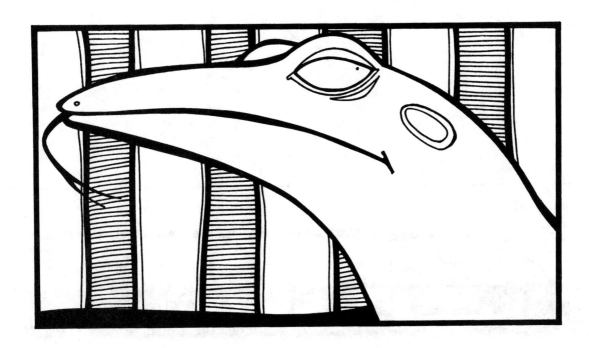

I'm Through! What Can I Do? Gr. 5–6
© The Learning Works, Inc.

Name _____

Design a Robot

Design a robot that will walk your dog, clean your bedroom, take out the garbage, or do some other task around the house. Add lights, propellers, arms, knobs, wheels, and/or other controls to your robot. Give your robot a name. On the back of your paper, describe how your robot works.

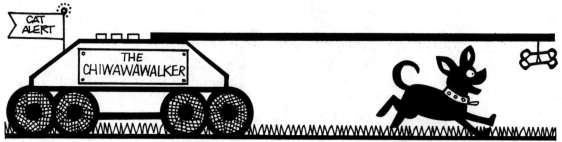

Name _____

Descriptions

Here are questions without any right or wrong answers. Take time to think about each question, and respond to each one.

What is the weight of a lie?

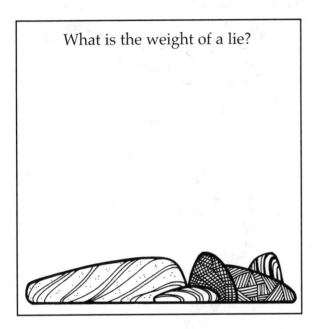

What is the sound of sadness?

What is the taste of happiness?

What is the color of friendship?

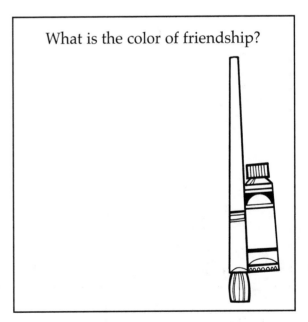

Just for Fun

On the back of your paper, make up four more questions using one of the following words in each question:

• feel   • memory   • silence   • size

Write a brief response to each of your questions.

I'm Through! What Can I Do? Gr. 5–6
© The Learning Works, Inc.

Name _____

Complete a Cheetah

Use the artwork on the right side of this drawing
as a guide to help you complete the cheetah.

Name _____

Half a Mask

Use the artwork on the left side of this drawing
as a guide to help you complete the mask.

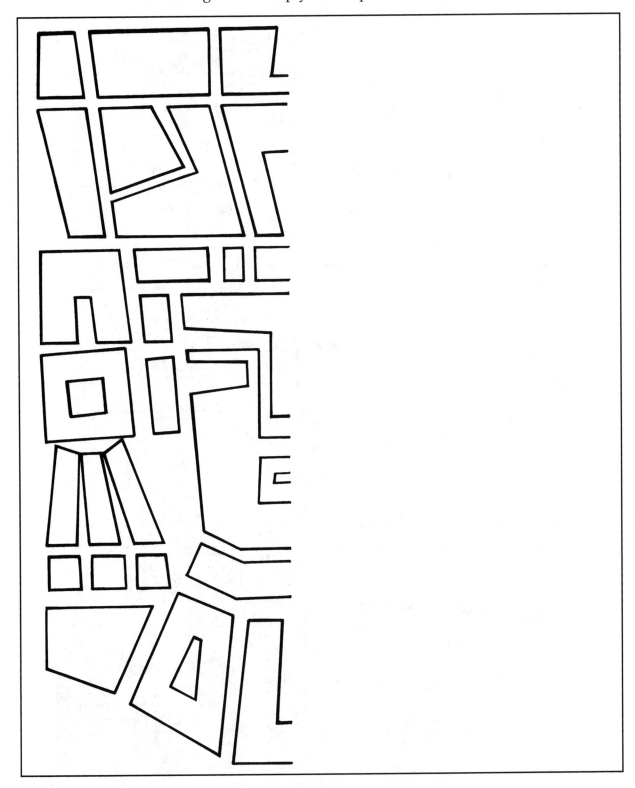

I'm Through! What Can I Do? Gr. 5–6
© The Learning Works, Inc.

Name _____

Draw a Dump Truck

On a separate sheet of paper, draw the dump truck
by following the step-by-step drawings.

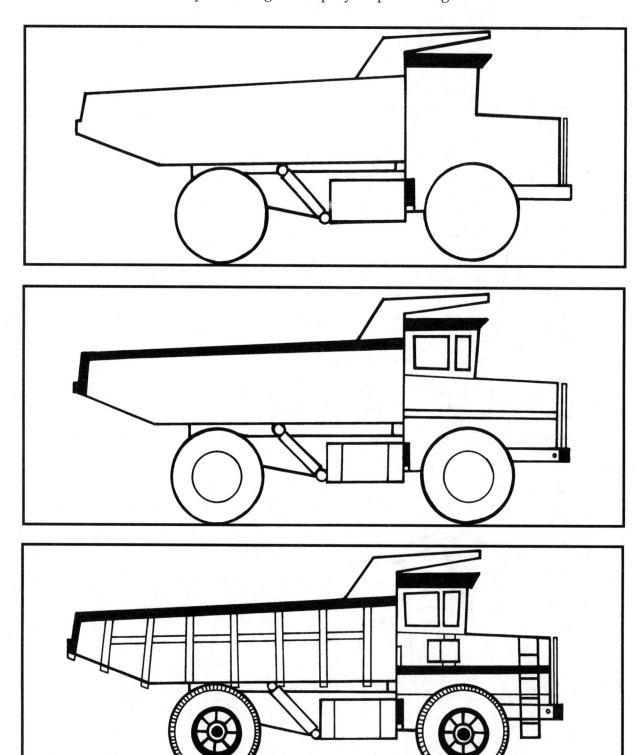

Name _____

Picture a Player

On a separate sheet of paper, draw the football player
by following the step-by-step drawings.

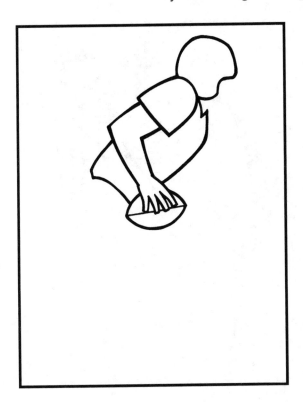

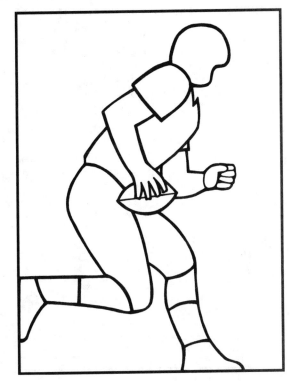

I'm Through! What Can I Do? Gr. 5–6
© The Learning Works, Inc.

Name _____

Sketch a Siamese Cat

On a separate sheet of paper, sketch a Siamese cat
by following the step-by-step drawings.

Design a Daisy

On a separate sheet of paper, design a daisy
by following the step-by-step drawings.

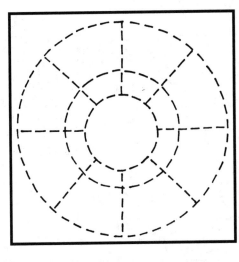

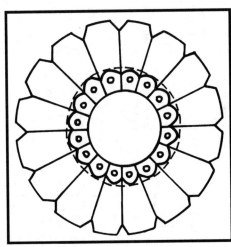

I'm Through! What Can I Do? Gr. 5–6
© The Learning Works, Inc.

Name _____

Fish Grid

To make a picture of a colorful tropical fish, copy the small drawings into the squares of the grid below. The numbers and letters tell where each drawing belongs. The first one (B1) has been done for you.

Name _____

Bird Grid

To make a picture of a familiar bird which may have a ten-foot wingspan, copy the small drawings into the squares of the grid below. The numbers and letters tell where each drawing belongs. The first one (B1) has been done for you.

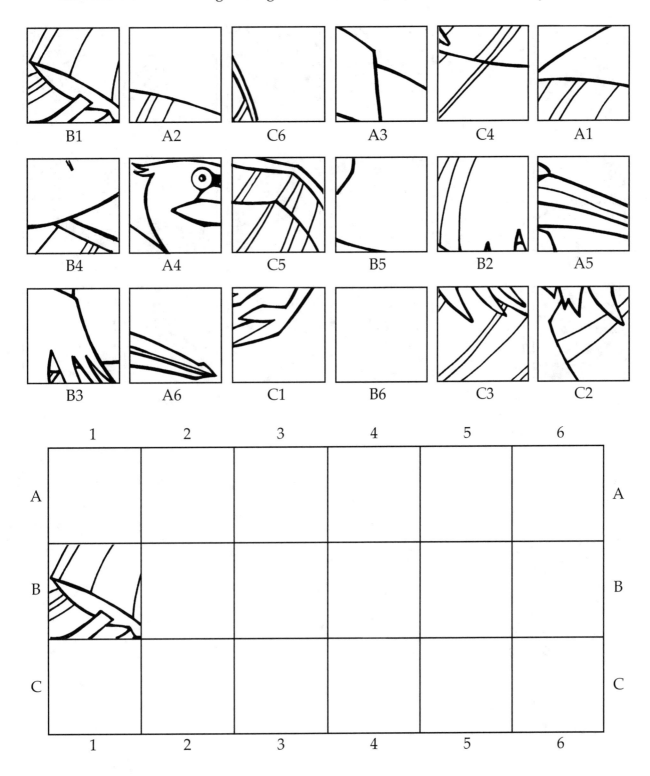

Name _____

Motorcycle Mosaic

To draw this motorcycle, you will need a circular template. Copy the small drawings into the squares of the grid below. The numbers and letters tell where each drawing belongs. The first one (B3) has been done for you.

Name _____

Mammoth Moth

Draw the other half of this Atlas moth to match the side that is completed. Color your moth when you are finished.

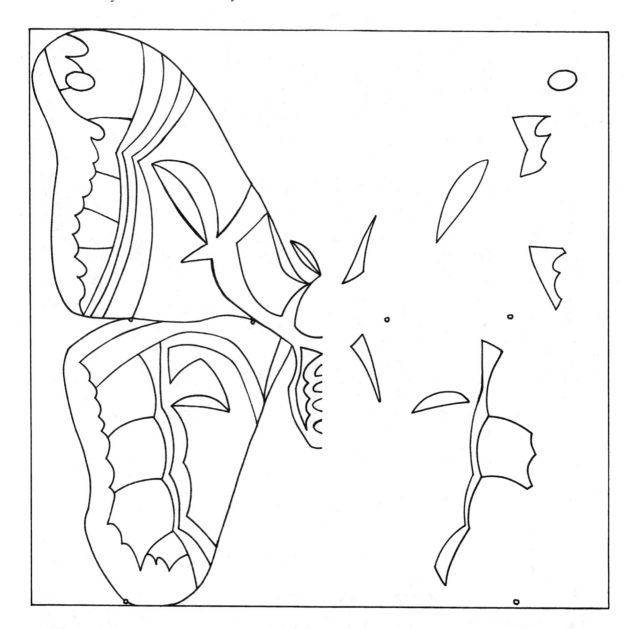

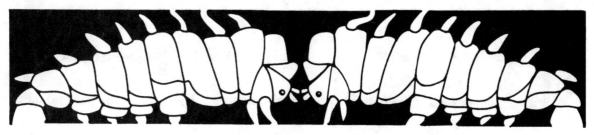

Nail Maze

Make a trail through the nails, entering and leaving at the arrows.

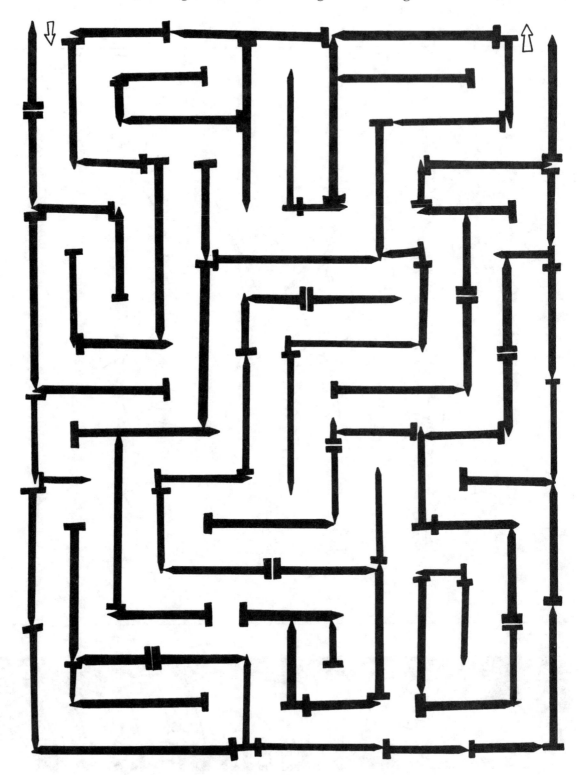

Name _____

Shoelace Race

"Run" this race with a friend. You will each start at one end of the lace and draw a line toward the black square. The first one there is the winner! (Hint: Use pens of two different colors.)

I'm Through! What Can I Do? Gr. 5–6
© The Learning Works, Inc.

Name _____

Through the Turtle

Draw a line through the maze starting and ending at the arrows.

Web Site

Can you escape from the web? Draw a line from the center to the edge.

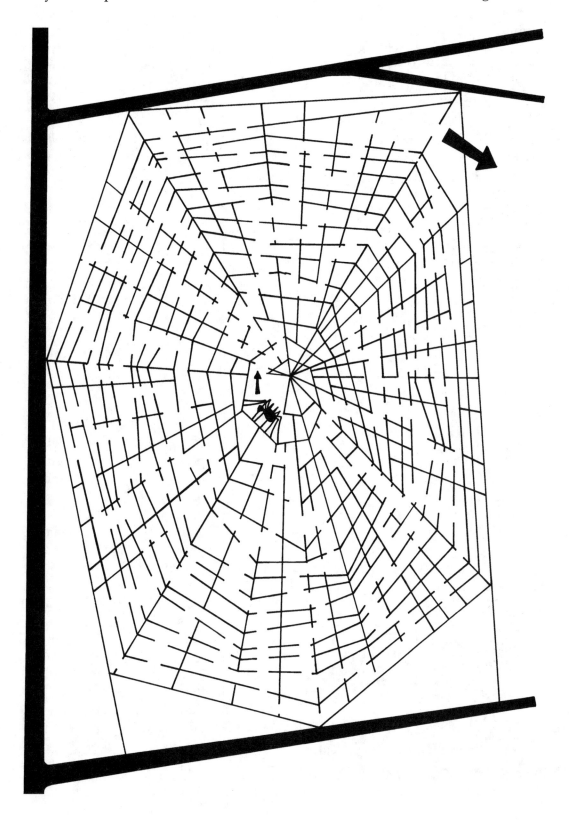

Answer Key

page 6 – Compound Capers

1. back
2. ball
3. down
4. hill
5. pan
6. one
7. space
8. vine
9. chair
10. break
11. place
12. basket
13. block
14. house
15. cat

page 7 – More Compound Capers

1. apple
2. side
3. bow
4. side
5. book
6. light
7. out
8. stream
9. cup
10. market
11. fork
12. fruit
13. band
14. room
15. skate

page 8 – Anagram Antics

1. deal, dale
2. each
3. worth
4. grown
5. dear, dare
6. shore
7. pace
8. stone, tones
9. spread, rasped, spared
10. spear, reaps, pares
11. night
12. tales, steal, least
13. react, crate, caret
14. rested
15. stream, tamers

page 9 – More Anagram Antics

1. dues, sued
2. rats, tars, arts
3. scare, cares, races
4. tame, team, mate
5. bare
6. garden, ranged
7. earns, nears
8. lance
9. rescue
10. slate, steal, tales
11. takes, stake
12. strap, traps
13. great
14. hears, shear, hares
15. section

Page 10 – Palindrome Challenge

Answers will vary; possible answers:

bib	radar
bob	refer
civic	rotor
dad	sees
did	solos
gag	toot
level	———————————
mom	Madam, I'm Adam.
noon	not a ton
peep	too hot to hoot
pop	Was it a cat I saw?
pup	we sew
race car	wet stew

page 11 – Find the Food

1. corn
2. peach
3. tomato
4. turnip
5. fish
6. toast
7. pear
8. potato
9. beef
10. tofu
11. beans
12. mango
13. banana
14. lemon
15. candy

page 12 – Hidden Animals

1. horse
2. lamb
3. leopard
4. goat
5. bat
6. hawk
7. bear
8. panda
9. jackal
10. camel
11. beaver
12. badger
13. ostrich
14. condor
15. toad

Answer Key

page 13 – Mystery Message
You can't judge a book by its cover.

page 14 – Letter Links
Answers will vary; possible answers:

are	new	sews
art	newer	swear
aware	news	tie
ear	rear	tier
era	renew	ties
kin	rink	tike
kit	sea	tries
kite	sear	war
kites	sense	ware
knew	senses	wares
knit	set	wart
near	sew	wear
net	sewer	wet

page 15 – More Letter Links
Answers will vary; possible answers:

aching	car	hinting
again	care	hit
age	chin	mint
aging	cigar	nab
aim	cub	nag
aiming	curb	rag
ant	cure	rage
are	each	raging
bag	ear	rain
ban	era	rang
bang	gain	range
bar	gait	reach
barb	garb	rear
bare	garbage	regain
bargain	gear	rub
barge	giant	ruin
bra	gin	tiger
brag	grain	timing
brain	grant	tin
bran	him	tinge
bureau	hint	tint

page 16 – Groupies

1.	life	7.	up
2.	house	8.	water
3.	hard	9.	down
4.	eye	10.	over
5.	back	11.	book
6.	class	12.	high

page 17 – Hide Five
Answers will vary.

page 18 – Alphabet Soup
Answers will vary; possible answers:

abet	hat	lots	sap
abets	hate	louse	sat
alpha	hats	oat	sate
ape	heat	oats	set
apes	heats	out	shape
apple	help	outs	slap
asp	helps	pal	slat
ate	hop	pale	slate
bale	hope	pales	slop
bales	hopes	pals	slope
base	hops	past	stab
bat	hose	pats	staple
bats	house	pea	step
beat	hut	peas	stub
beats	huts	peat	tab
belt	lab	phase	table
blot	labs	plate	tables
blots	lap	plates	tabs
blouse	laps	poet	tap
bop	lapse	poets	tape
bops	last	pop	tapes
bus	late	pops	taps
but	let	post	those
east	lets	pot	top
eat	lob	pots	tub
eats	lobes	pout	tuba
hale	lobs	pouts	tube
halt	lop	pulse	tubes
halts	lops	sable	tubs
has	lost	sale	ups
hasp	lot	salt	use

I'm Through! What Can I Do? Gr. 5–6
© The Learning Works, Inc.

Answer Key

page 21 – Number Roundup #1

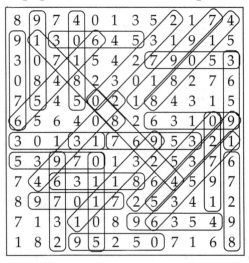

page 22 – Number Roundup #2

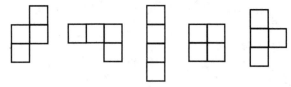

page 23 – Score a Home Run
Clockwise starting from top: 2, 8, 6, 7, 3, 4, 9, 5

page 24 – Find Five

page 25 – Catch a Thief
16, 8, 5, 13, 2, 11

page 26 – Number Pattern Puzzle #1
1. 33
2. 23
3. 34
4. 40
5. 8
6. 144
7. 64
8. 336
9. 31
10. 160

page 27 – Number Pattern Puzzle #2
1. 81
2. 68
3. 72
4. 32
5. 44
6. 56
7. 13
8. 75
9. 52
10. 34

page 28 – Geometric Challenge
1. J and F
2. E, H, and L
3. I
4. C
5. N
6. M
7. A
8. K
9. B
10. G, D, and M

page 29 – Pick a Set
Boxes 2 and 5 are the same.

page 30 – Marathon Winner
Juanita is the winner – number 7869.

page 31 – Bingo Bongo
The fourth row (67, 80, 9, 95, 4)
is the matching row.

page 33 – Candy Match
Fruit slices 2 and 4
Candy sticks 1 and 5
Taffy pieces 3 and 5
Gumdrops 2 and 3

page 34 – Pizza Pieces
A - 1 and 4
B - 3 and 5
C - 2 and 5

page 35 – Matching Marbles
A - 8 and 13
B - 8 and 10
C - 1 and 15
D - 4 and 9

Answer Key

page 36 – Bagel, Bongo, and Bounce

page 38 – Legs and No Legs

page 37 – I See!

page 39 – Separate the Sounds

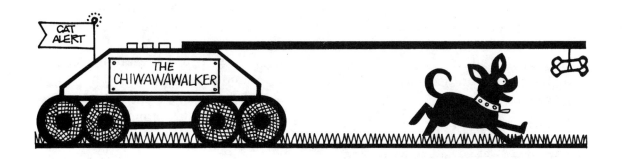

Answer Key

page 44–45 – Junk Drawer Jumble
The eight things that were not in the drawer are buckle, clothespin, feather, fork, glue, matches, scissors, and tape.

page 46–47 – Focus on the Flags
1. Jamaica
2. Canada and Jamaica
3. Rwanda
4. Panama
5. Switzerland
6. Rwanda
7. Panama
8. Cyprus
9. Lebanon
10. six

page 52 – What's Hot? – What's Not?
Answers will vary, but here are the things the words in "What's Hot?" have in common:
1. start and end with vowels
2. yellow foods
3. things to wear on the head
4. all contain the letter "u"
5. words with one syllable
6. start and end with same letter
7. things to wear on the feet
8. all are names of foods
9. all hold things
10. white foods

page 53 – More What's Hot? – What's Not?
Answers will vary, but here are the things the words in "What's Hot?" have in common:
1. round things
2. green foods
3. woodwind instruments
4. names with two syllables
5. words with two consecutive vowels
6. words with the letter "y"
7. words with double consonants
8. compound words
9. all adjectives
10. first two letters are next to each other in the alphabet

page 54 – Odd Word Out
1. d. derbies
2. d. tackle
3. a. gallon
4. c. vault
5. b. tuba
6. c. clock
7. d. radio
8. a. bracelet
9. b. toga
10. c. sponge
11. d. chef
12. a. dense

page 55 – More Odd Word Out
1. c. radius
2. b. putt
3. b. borzoi
4. a. petunia
5. c. diamond
6. a. puck
7. d. sycamore
8. b. palmetto
9. c. army
10. a. treble
11. b. rat
12. d. larynx

page 56 – Nature Category Game
Answers will vary.

page 57 – Geography Category Game
Answers will vary.

page 58 – Leisure Time Category Game
Answers will vary.

page 59 – Just for Fun Category Game
Answers will vary.

page 60 – The Bolobo Bug
The bolobo bug is saying "mizz."

page 61 – Choose the Shoes
The shoes you end up buying are called "Hurricane."

page 62–63 – Mitzi la Foo-Foo
Mitzi is #6.

page 64–65 – The Bird Watcher
Ima spotted a cardinal.

page 66 – Mystery Vacation
The Clark family is headed to Maine.

page 67 – Elegant Eggs
1. Elmo
2. Elena
3. Ernie
4. Eli
5. Eseza
6. Evan
7. Emma
8. Elisa
9. Eddie
10. Eric